Supporting
Literacy

FOR AGES 6–7

Andrew Brodie

Introduction

Supporting Literacy is aimed at all those who work with children who have been identified as needing 'additional' or 'different' literacy support. It can be used by anyone working with children who fall into this category, whether you are a teacher, classroom assistant or parent.

Typically the six to seven-year-old children for whom the book is intended will be working at the levels expected of Reception or Year 1 children or may simply need extra help in tackling the standard of work expected of Year 2. Their difficulties may be short term, and overcome with extra practice and support on a one to one or small group basis, or they may be long term where such support enables them to make progress but at a level behind their peer group. The activities in this book provide exactly what these children need – plenty of repetition and practice of basic skills, often covering the same ground but in a slightly different way. For this reason, you might decide to use the worksheets in a different order or just select the sheets that are suitable for the child or group of children you are working with. All the activities can be used on their own or alongside other literacy schemes that are already established within your school.

The worksheets are simple and self-explanatory and the instruction text is deliberately kept to a minimum to make the pages easy for adults to use and less daunting for children to follow. At the bottom of each page 'Notes for teachers' summarise the purpose of the activity and the learning target that is being addressed. Suggestions for additional activities are included if appropriate.

Most of the worksheets are based upon the National Literacy Strategy (NLS) objectives but some, where possible and relevant, are linked to other aspects of the curriculum. Through many years of experience of working with special needs children, the authors have been able to select the areas that these children find most difficult and provide useful activities that specifically address these stumbling blocks. Accordingly, and as set out below, most of the worksheets are centred around the word level strand of the Literacy Strategy.

The main targets addressed in this book are:
- Revising the NLS high frequency words for Reception specified in the National Literacy Strategy
- Beginning to read and spell the high frequency words for Years 1 and 2
- Spelling some regularly used words through the use of mnemonics: e.g. for 'because': big elephants can always upset small elephants
- Checking knowledge of initial letter sounds and ability to sound out and write these letters
- Checking knowledge of letter names/alphabetical order/simple dictionary work
- Knowing alphabet in upper and lower case
- Picking out rhyming words in a poem
- Practising cvc, ccvc, cvcc words and ccvcc words through examining the consonant digraph endings ff, ll, ss, ck, ng, ld nd lk nk sk lp mp sp ct ft lt nt zz st xt lf
- Practising cvc, ccvc, cvcc words and ccvcc words through examining the consonant digraph initial blends bl br cl cr dr dw fl fr gl gr pl pr sc sk sl sm sn sp st tr
- Practising some vowel digraphs, e.g. ai ee oo or ar ir oi ou ay
- Writing one or two sentences unaided but with prompts, using capital letters for the starts of sentences and full stops at the ends.
- Knowing the vowels (+y) and that there is at least one vowel in each word
- Using the terms vowel and consonant
- Keeping writing a uniform size and with a space between each word

However you decide to use these sheets and in whatever context, it is worth remembering that children generally achieve the greatest success in an atmosphere of support and encouragement. Praise from a caring adult can be the best reward for children's efforts. The worksheets and activities in this book will provide many opportunities for children to enjoy their successes. The resulting increase in self-esteem will make a difference to their school work and other areas of school life too.

Individual record sheet

Name:

Worksheet	Teaching and learning objective	Target achieved	Needs more practice
1-2	To read words with initial blend **st**		
3-4	To read words with initial blend **tr**		
5-6	To read words with initial blend **cl**		
7-8	To read words with initial blend **fl**		
9-10	To read words with initial blend **fr**		
11-12	To identify separate phonemes in words containing vowel **a**		
13-14	To identify separate phonemes in words containing vowel **e**		
15-16	To identify separate phonemes in words containing vowel **i**		
17-18	To identify separate phonemes in words containing vowel **o**		
19-20	To identify separate phonemes in words containing vowel **u**		
21-24	To identify rhyming words in a poem		
25-26	To learn to spell 'they', 'because' and 'said'		
27-33	To learn alphabetical order, and to identify initial letters in words		
34-35	To know the word ending **ng**		
36	To know the word endings: **ss, ff, ll**		
37	To know the word endings: **ng, ck, ld**		
38	To know the word endings: **nd, nk, lk**		
39	To know the word endings: **mp, nt, zz**		
40	To know the word endings: **sk, lp, sp**		
41	To know the word endings: **ft, rk, ct**		
42	To know the word endings: **lt, xt, lf**		
43	To know the initial blends: **bl, gl, pl**		
44	To know the initial blends: **br, cr, dr**		
45	To know the initial blends: **sw, sc, sk**		
46	To know the initial blends: **gr, pr, sl**		
47	To know the initial blends: **sm, sn, sp**		
48	To read and write words needed in science work on growing plants		
49	To read and write words needed in geography and history work on 'the seaside'		
50	To read questions and to write complete sentences related to in geography and history work on 'the seaside'		

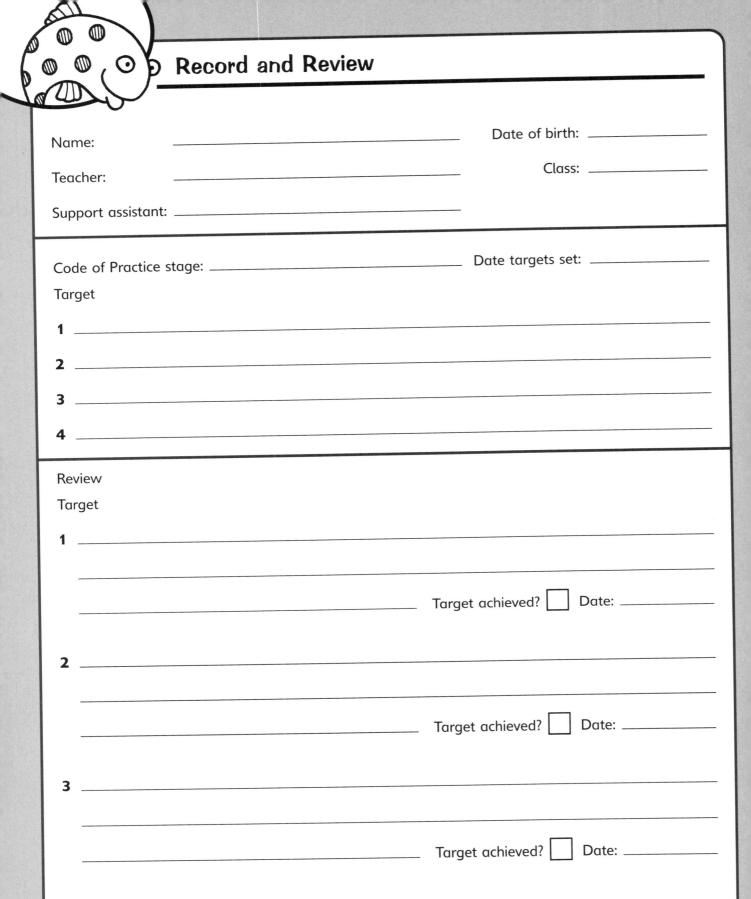

Record and Review

Name: _____ Date of birth: _____

Teacher: _____ Class: _____

Support assistant: _____

Code of Practice stage: _____ Date targets set: _____

Target

1 _____

2 _____

3 _____

4 _____

Review

Target

1 _____
_____
_____ Target achieved? ☐ Date: _____

2 _____
_____
_____ Target achieved? ☐ Date: _____

3 _____
_____
_____ Target achieved? ☐ Date: _____

4 _____
_____
_____ Target achieved? ☐ Date: _____

Content of the worksheets

The activities in this book are based on 'tracking back' in the Literacy Framework to provide appropriate materials for Year 2 pupils who need extra attention and support. Each worksheet features a main activity and most also include a subsidiary activity – the 'garden path'.

The garden path, which appears in a variety of different guises, contains nine NLS high frequency words for reading practice. Each path introduces a new word and provides practice of several words that have appeared on previous paths. As a child reads each word successfully they can colour the appropriate shape on the path. This can also serve as a useful tool for recording a child's progress over a series of lessons.

Worksheets 1-10 provide practice of the common initial blends st, tr, cl, fl and fr. (Further work on initial blends appears on worksheets 43 to 47.)

Worksheets 11-20 concentrate on the medial vowel sounds, used in cvc words, in ccvc words, in cvcc words and in ccvcc words.

In **Worksheets 21-24** the children are asked to find rhyming words, using their knowledge of phonic blends.

Worksheets 25-26 focus on the challenging words 'because', 'said' and 'they'.

Worksheets 27-33 introduce alphabetical order. Pupils can practise the alphabet as well as making use of the alphabet to write words in order. The words used are all taken from the high frequency words for Years 1 and 2.

Worksheets 34-42 cover most of the final consonant clusters recommended in the Literacy Strategy while worksheets 43 to 47 cover the initial blends.

Worksheets 48-50 contain cross-curricular tasks, providing practice of words and sentences associated with some of the topic areas that are likely to be covered in Key Stage 1. These three sheets do not contain 'garden path' words.

Resource sheets A-I The final section of the book contains resource sheets to be made into flashcards for the first 45 NLS high frequency words for Reception pupils together with all of the recommended words for Years 1 and 2. This collection of words includes all those on the 'garden paths' and enables you to create sentences with the pupils. The children will, of course, need reminding that the initial letter of a sentence must be a capital letter and that the sentence should normally end with a full stop (the exceptions to this rule being when the sentence ends with a question mark or exclamation mark).

Name: _____ Date: _____

Cut out the jigsaw pieces and match them up to make words.

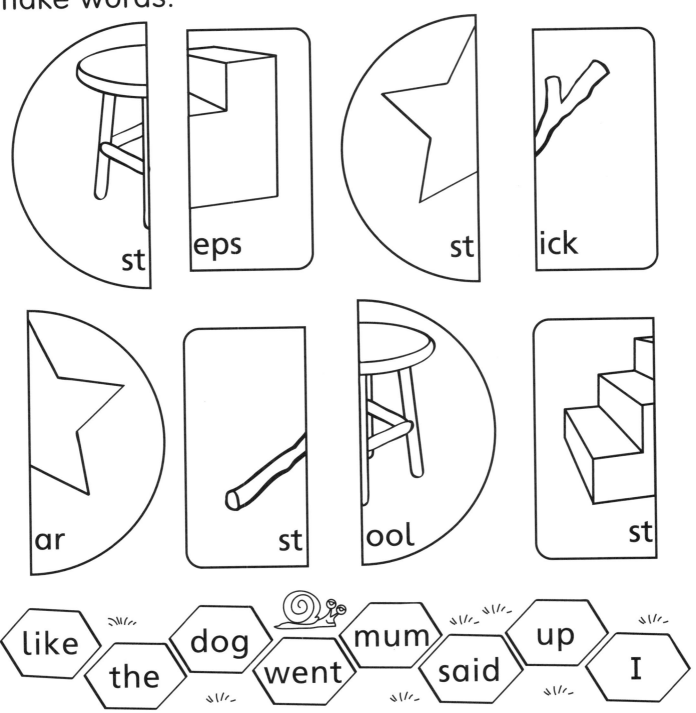

Notes for teachers

Target: To read words with initial blend **st**

Encourage the children to 'sound out' the blend. Demonstrate how it can be matched with one of the endings provided. Very often those pupils experiencing difficulty with reading skills may also be the ones who find accurate cutting a challenge too. It is for you to decide whether your goup will gain more benefit from cutting out their own jigsaw shapes with adult help, or whether to prepare the pieces beforehand. Once the children have completed the four words ask them to think of more words that start with **st**. You may need to supply some examples: *stop, stem, stir, steep, still*. Children could stick the completed word puzzles in their books and write the other words they have found underneath. You could use the **st** words on this page with the 'garden path' words to make simple sentences.

Andrew Brodie: Supporting Literacy © A & C Black Publishers Ltd. 2006

Match the correct word to each picture.

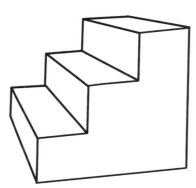

- - - - - - - - - - - - - - - - - - -   - - - - - - - - - - - - - - - - - - -

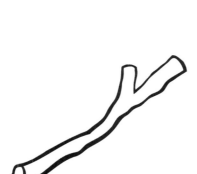

- - - - - - - - - - - - - - - - - - -   - - - - - - - - - - - - - - - - - - -

| stick | steps | stool | star |

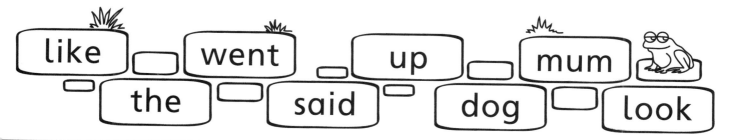

Notes for teachers

Target: To read words with initial blend **st**

This page reinforces work from Worksheet 1 and uses the same four **st** words. The children can either write the words under the pictures or cut them out and stick them in place. As before, ask the children to think of more **st** words. Possibilities include: *stairs, steel, stop, start.* Simple sentences may, once again, be made by using the target words with the 'garden path' words, e.g. *The dog went up the step.* Take the opportunity to encourage the children to use a capital letter at the start of the sentence and a full stop at the end.

Name: _____   Date: _____

Cut out the jigsaw pieces and match them up to make words.

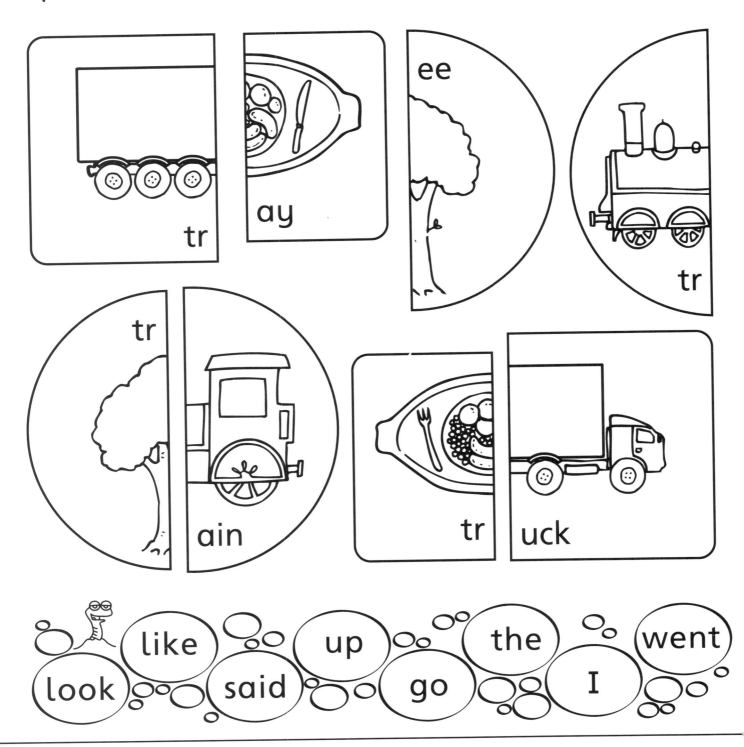

8   Andrew Brodie: Supporting Literacy © A & C Black Publishers Ltd. 2006

Notes for teachers
Target: To read words with initial consonant blend **tr**
Encourage the children to sound out the blend. Demonstrate how it can be matched with one of the endings provided. Once the children have completed the four word puzzles ask them to think of more words that start with **tr**. You may need to supply some examples: *trust, trot, true.* Children could stick the completed puzzles in their books and write the other **tr** words they have found underneath. You could use the **tr** words on this page with the 'garden path' words to make simple sentences e.g. *I went on the train.*

Copy the words. Finish the pictures.

tree

truck

- -

tray

train

- -

went   look   like   said   go   up   dog   come

Notes for teachers
Target: To read words with the initial consonant blend **tr**.
This page reinforces the work from the previous worksheet. Encourage the children to think of other **tr** words as before.
Ensure children form letters correctly as they copy the words on the sheet. Simple sentences can be made using the **tr** words
with the 'garden path' words and the additional word 'the', e.g. *The dog went up the tree.*

Name: Date:

Read the words. Copy the words.
Cut out the pictures.
Stick the pictures with the correct words.

clown

cloud

- - - - - - - - - - - - - - - - - - - -

- - - - - - - - - - - - - - - - - - - -

clap

clock

- - - - - - - - - - - - - - - - - - - -

- - - - - - - - - - - - - - - - - - - -

go   look   said   mum

come   went   like   yes

Notes for teachers
Target: To read words with the initial consonant blend **cl**
Encourage the children to sound out the blend. Once they have stuck the four pictures in the correct places, ask them to
think of more words that start with **cl**. You may need to supply some examples if the child is unable to think of any, e.g.
cling, clog, cluck, clear. You could use the **cl** words in conjunction with the 'garden path' words and the word 'the' to
make simple sentences e.g. *"Look," said the clown.*

Andrew Brodie: Supporting Literacy © A & C Black Publishers Ltd. 2006

Use the words to make a sentence for each picture.

| I | see | at | go | clown |

| the | clock | and | a | look |

- -

- -

- -

- -

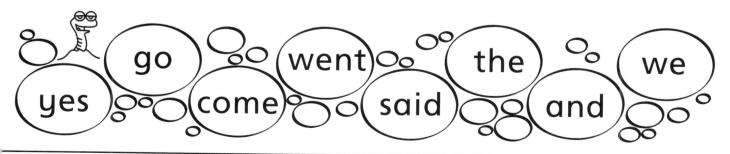

yes go come went said the and we

Notes for teachers

Target: To read words with the initial consonant cluster **cl**

This sheet reinforces the work on **cl** words from the previous sheet. You can choose whether the children should copy the words they need, or whether to cut out and stick the words on. Encourage children to experiment with a range of simple sentences. They can use the 'garden path' words in addition to the words at the top of the page. Sentences could include: *See a clown. Look at the clock. "Come," said the clown.*

Name: _____

Date: _____

Colour the pictures.
Cut out the pictures.
Stick the pictures in the correct places.

Notes for teachers
Target: To read words with initial consonant cluster **fl**
After completing the activity on the page ask children to think of other words beginning with the **fl** blend. Examples you could supply, if children have difficulty thinking of any, might include: *fling, flat, flute, floor.* Make simple sentences using the 'garden path' words, the **fl** words and 'the', e.g. *The fly went up.*

Name: _____ **Date:** _____

Copy the writing.
Colour the pictures.

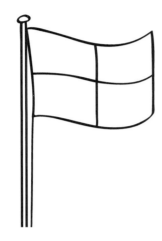

The flag is flying.

The fly is on the flower.

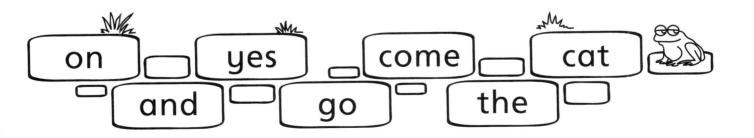

on   yes   come   cat

and   go   the

Notes for teachers

Target: To read words with the initial consonant cluster **fl**. To read simple sentences.
As before, encourage the children to think of other **fl** words. When copying the sentences ensure children form letters correctly and leave spaces between words. Additional activities could include making further sentences using the **fl** words in conjunction with 'garden path' words.

Name: _____

Date: _____

Copy the words.

The frog is on the leaf.

The fly is on the cat.

----

cat   on   and   we   yes   go   said   play

Notes for teachers

Target: To read words with initial consonant cluster **fr**. To form lower case letters correctly.
Encourage children to think of other words beginning with the consonant blend **fr**. If the children are unable to think of any you may need to supply examples. These could include *fridge, fright, frill, frost*. Try to ensure that they are hearing the difference between the sounds 'fr' and 'fl'. Make other sentences by including some of the words from the 'garden path' e.g. *The cat and the frog.*

Put the correct word with each picture.
Colour the pictures.

fringe

friend

frog

from

fruit

fry

play   cat   on   and   we   yes   look   dad

Notes for teachers

Target: To read words beginning with initial consonant cluster **fr**

Encourage the children to try to read all the given words. Some may need considerable support to do this. Children can either cut out and stick the correct words into place, or write the correct words. Letters should be formed correctly if the words are written. An additional activity would be to use the remaining **fr** words on the sheet in conjunction with the 'garden path' words and the word 'the' to make simple sentences, e.g. *The frog and the cat fry fruit.*

Andrew Brodie: Supporting Literacy © A & C Black Publishers Ltd. 2006

Name: _____   Date: _____

Cut out the jigsaw pieces and match them up to make words.

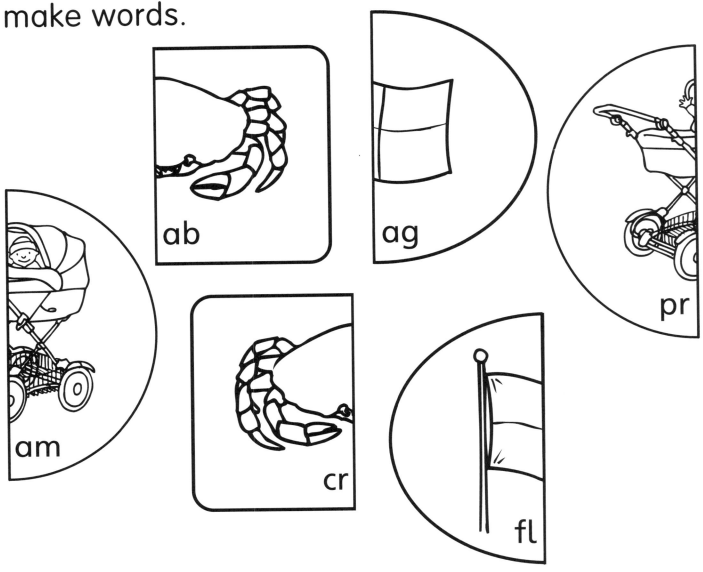

ab

ag

pr

am

cr

fl

Read this sentence: A crab saw a flag.

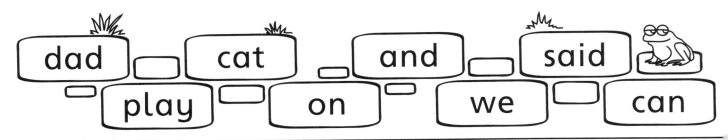

dad   cat   and   said

play   on   we   can

Notes for teachers

Target: To identify separate phonemes in words containing vowel **a**

It is for you to decide whether your pupils will gain more benefit from cutting out their own jigsaw shapes with adult help, or whether to prepare the pieces beforehand. Children could stick the completed puzzles into their books and write the words they have found underneath. Ensure they read the words they have found correctly, particularly noticing the 'a' sound in each one. Children can also use the words on this page in conjunction with the 'garden path' words to make simple sentences e.g. *Dad saw a crab and a flag.*

Name: _____ **Date:** _____

Put the correct word in each sentence.

Here is a _____ .

crab

crash

A _____ is flying in the wind.

than

that

The baby is in the _____ .

pram

flat

flag

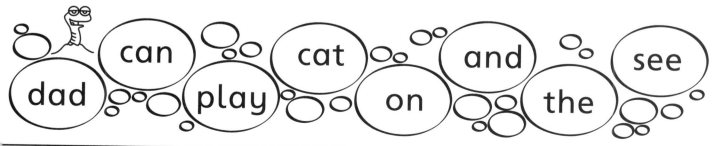

dad can cat play on and the see

Notes for teachers

Target: Target: To identify separate phonemes in words containing vowel **a**
Encourage children (with support as needed) to read all the words in the boxes noting the 'a' sound in each of the words.
They should write the correct words in the spaces forming the letters of the words correctly. All the words on the page,
including the 'garden path' words, can then be used to make other simple sentences, e.g. *A crab and a cat can play.*

Name: _____   Date: _____

Write the correct word under each picture.

WORD BANK

| ten | men | bed | leg | pet |

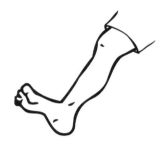

-------------------   -------------------   -------------------

-------------------   -------------------

Read the sentence: Ten men fed pets.

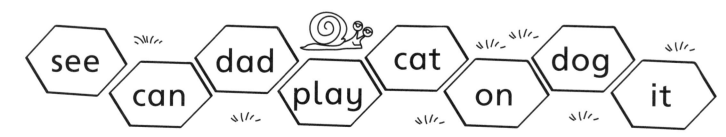

see   can   dad   play   cat   on   dog   it

Notes for teachers
Target: To identify separate phonemes in words containing vowel **e**
Children should read the words noting the short 'e' sound in each one. They should be encouraged to think of other words with that sound, e.g. *net, get, stem, neck.* Ensure that pupils form the letters correctly when copying the words. Use the **e** words with the 'garden path' words to make sentences. Take the opportunity to encourage the child to use a capital letter at the start of the sentence and a full stop at the end.

Draw a picture to go with each sentence.
Copy the sentences.

The bell fell on
ten shells.

This is a red shed.

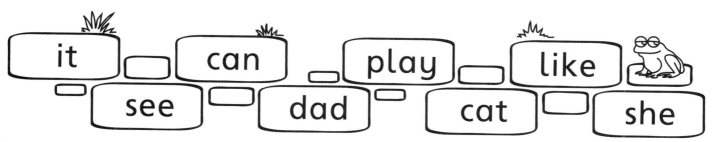

it   can   play   like

see   dad   cat   she

Notes for teachers
Target: To identify separate phonemes in words containing vowel **e**
Children should be encouraged to form letters correctly when copying the sentences. Children can use the words from
the two given sentences with the 'garden path' words to form more sentences of their own, e.g. *Dad can see the red shed.*
The cat can play on the shed.

Name: _____   **Date:** _____

Colour the pictures. Cut out the pictures. Put them in the correct spaces.

I sit in the bin.

A pig can dig.

A tin with a big lid.

can   dad   it   play   she   see   the   in

Notes for teachers
Target: To identify separate phonemes in words containing vowel **i**.
Ensure pupils read the sentences before starting to colour and cut out the pictures. Pupils should notice the 'i' sound in most of the words they are reading. Some children may need help with cutting out.

Draw the pictures.
Copy the words.

Six fish in a dish.

This is a stick in the sink.

in   it   she   see   can   dad   go   away

Notes for teachers

Target: To identify separate phonemes in words containing vowel **i**

Children should read the sentences carefully before beginning to draw the pictures or copy the writing. They should be encouraged to note the 'i' sound in the appropriate words. Extra sentences can be made using the sentence words and the 'garden path' words on this page, e.g. *Dad can see six fish in the sink.*

Name: _____

Date: _____

Make the words. Read the words.
Write them down.

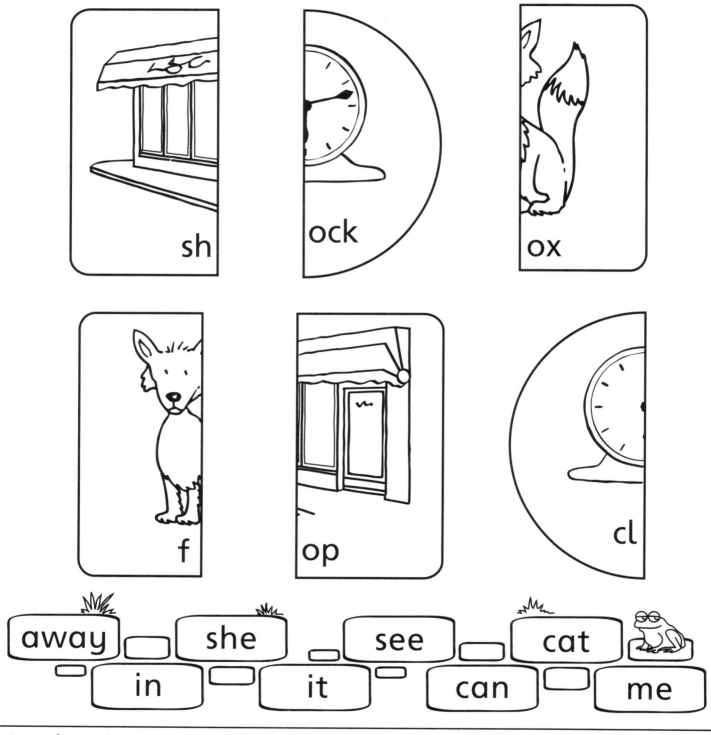

sh

ock

ox

f

op

cl

away   she   see   cat

in   it   can   me

Notes for teachers

Target: To identify separate phonemes in words containing vowel **o**

Encourage the children to sound out the phonemes as they read the puzzle words. They should notice the 'o' sound in each of the words. It is for you to decide whether your children will gain more benefit from cutting out their own puzzle pieces or whether to prepare the pieces for use beforehand. If the child has cut out the puzzle pieces he/she will need to write the words on a separate piece of paper or in an exercise book. Use the target words plus the 'garden path' words and the word 'the' to make simple sentences, e.g. *The fox can see the shop.*

Draw the pictures.
Copy the words.

A fox in a frock.

A clock on a log.

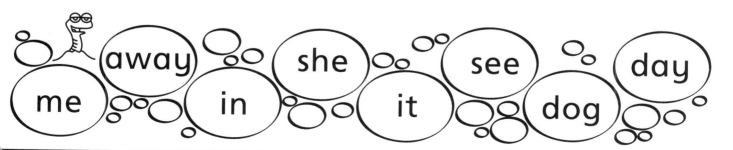

Notes for teachers
Target: To identify separate phonemes in words containing vowel **o**
Children should read the phrases and note the **o** words. You should ensure they form letters correctly when copying the words. Use the 'sentence words' plus the 'garden path words' and 'the' to make simple sentences, e.g. *See the dog on a log.* Take the opportunity to encourage the children to use a capital letter at the start of each sentence and a full stop at the end.

Name: **Date:**

Use the words to label the pictures.

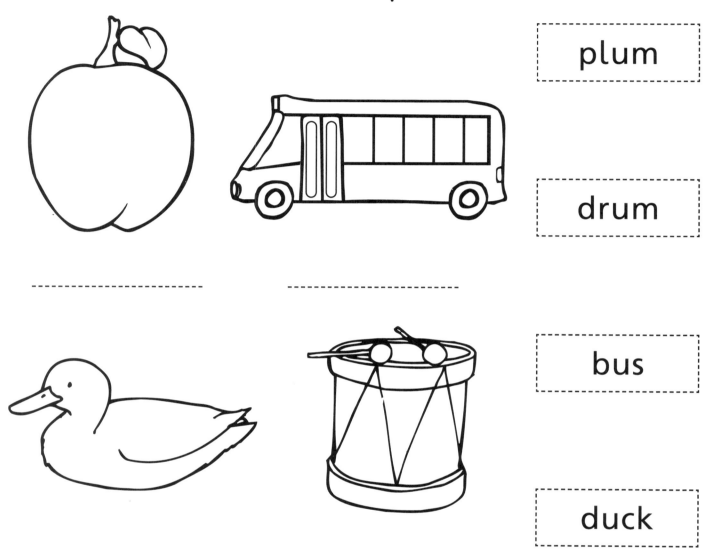

plum

drum

bus

duck

----------------   ----------------

----------------   ----------------

Read the sentence: A duck sat on a bus.

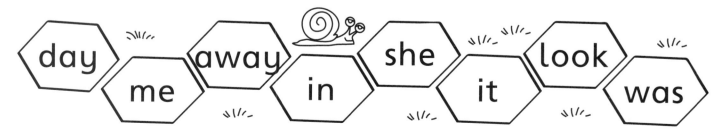

day   away   she   look

me   in   it   was

Notes for teachers

Target: To identify separate phonemes in words containing vowel **u**

Pupils should read the words noting the 'u' sound in each one. You may ask the children to either cut out the words and stick them under the correct pictures, or write the words under the pictures. When this activity has been completed ask children to think of other words with the 'u' sound, e.g. *bun, fun*. Use the target words plus 'garden path' words and the word 'the', to make simple sentences, e.g. *The drum was in the bus.*

Read the rhyme.

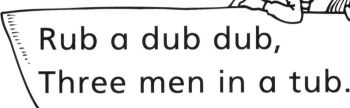

Rub a dub dub,
Three men in a tub.

Use the words to
label the pictures.

| duck | drum |
| bus | mug |

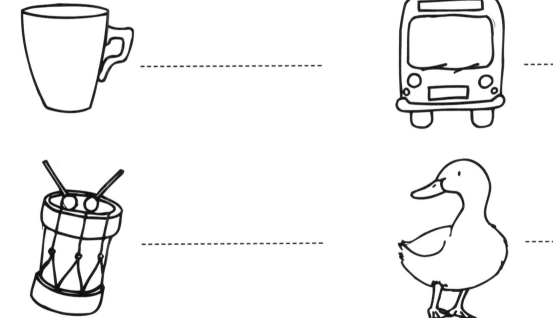

\- - - - - - - - - - - - - - - -   \- - - - - - - - - - - - - - - -

\- - - - - - - - - - - - - - - -   \- - - - - - - - - - - - - - - -

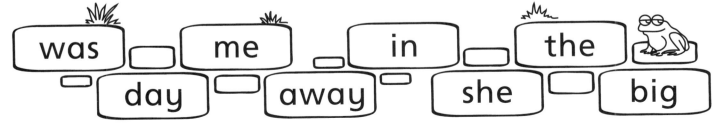

was   me   in   the

day   away   she   big

Notes for teachers

Target: To identify separate phonemes in words containing vowel **u**
Children should, when reading the rhyme, note the 'u' words. When they copy the words onto the labelling lines you should ensure they form their letters correctly. The target words, the words in the rhyme and the 'garden path' words can be used to make sentences, e.g. *The duck was in the big tub.*

Name: _____   Date: _____

Choose the words to finish the rhymes.

WORD BANK

sleep   truck

Counting sheep

will help you _____.

I saw a duck

sitting in a _____.

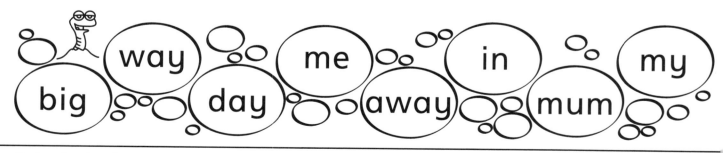

big way day me away in mum my

Notes for teachers

Target: To pick out rhyming words in a poem

Children should be encouraged to read each of the rhymes several times to hear the same sound in the rhyming words. They should also look at the same ending of each written rhyming word. Ensure the children form letters correctly when copying the words to complete the rhymes. Use the words from the rhymes and the 'garden path' words to make extra sentences.

Read the words.
Put the rhyming words in the correct shape.

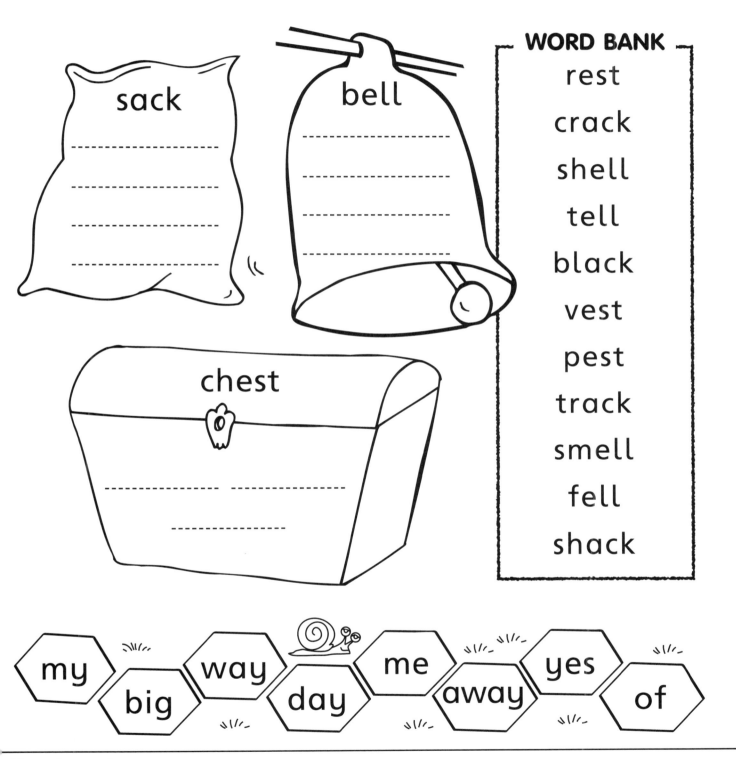

sack

----

bell

----

chest
---------------- ----------------

WORD BANK

rest

crack

shell

tell

black

vest

pest

track

smell

fell

shack

my big way day me away yes of

Notes for teachers

Target: To pick out rhyming words

Pupils should first identify the words already in each of the shapes. Then they should read each of the words on the right hand side of the page and copy these words into the correct places. If writing the words, you should ensure that children form the letters correctly. They should then be encouraged to look at each set of rhyming words and recognise the pattern of the word endings. Use the rhyming words, the word 'the' and the 'garden path' words to make simple sentences.

Name: _____

Date: _____

Find words to make rhymes.

WORD BANK

clown   gown   fox   hill   box   Jill

Jack and _____
went up the _____.

I saw a _____ in a
long red _____.

A big red _____
jumped into a _____.

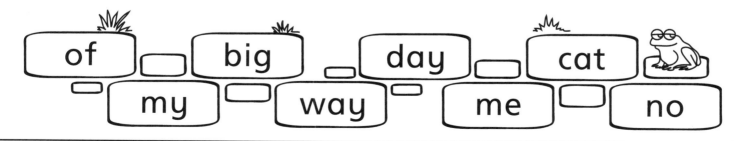

of   □   big   □   day   □   cat
□   my   □   way   □   me   □   no

Notes for teachers
Target: To pick out rhyming words in a poem
Children should be helped to identify the appropriate rhyming words by both sound and appearance. They should also check the rhymes for some sense. Use these words plus the 'garden path' words to make more sentences.

Read the rhyme. Draw the picture.

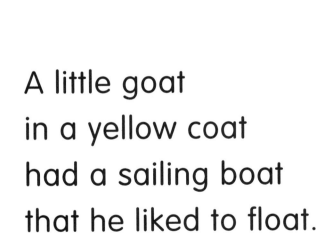

A little goat
in a yellow coat
had a sailing boat
that he liked to float.

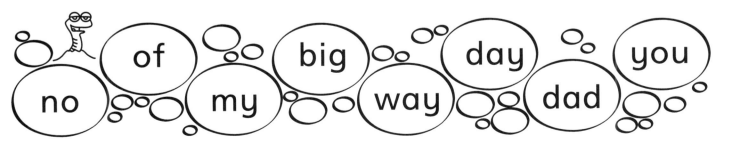

Notes for teachers
Target: To identify rhymes in a poem
Let the children read the poem a number of times allowing them to hear the rhymes at the end of the lines. They should also be encouraged to look at the written ending of the rhyming words. The words of the poem plus the 'garden path' words can be used to make other sentences.

Name: _____   **Date:** _____

Learn to spell these tricky words:

they   **said**   **because**

Use these to help you.

s	silly
a	animals
i	in
d	daisies

b	big
e	elephants
c	can
a	always
u	upset
s	small
e	elephants

t	tame
h	hens
e	eat
y	yoghurt

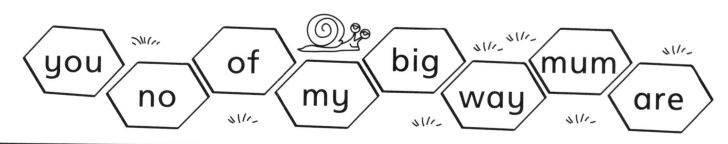

you   no   of   my   big   way   mum   are

Notes for teachers
Target: Learn to **they said because**
These mnemonics will need a lot of playful repetition to ensure they are known well enough to help with spelling. It is important that these common irregular words are correctly spelled from the earliest stage. Use the target words and the 'garden path' words to make sentences.

Use the three tricky words to complete the sentences.

My mum _____ it was time for tea.

Three boys ran.
Then _____ jumped
into a box.

I like spiders _____
they are cuddly.

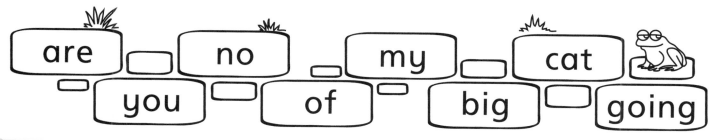

are no my cat
you of big going

Notes for teachers

Target: Learn to spell **they said because**

Children should practise the mnemonics they learned for spelling 'they', 'because' and 'said' before looking at this activity sheet. They should be reminded that these are the 'tricky words' that they practised in the last lesson. Children should read the sentences and work out which word goes in which position. Words should be written with letters formed correctly. Use all the words on this page (including the 'garden path' words) to make extra sentences.

Name: _____

Date: _____

Read the letters of the alphabet. Begin at the top of the snake.
Put the missing letter in each word.

_ est

_ pple

a b c d e f g h i j k l m n o p q r s t u v w x y z

_ ree

_ ebra

_ mbrella

going   are   you   no   of   my   play   to

Notes for teachers
Target: To look at alphabetical order, and to identify initial letters in words
Help the children to enjoy reading the letters of the alphabet in the correct order. Pupils should write the initial letters
(formed correctly) in each word. They can use the words, the word 'the' and the 'garden path' words to make sentences.

     Andrew Brodie: Supporting Literacy © A & C Black Publishers Ltd. 2006

a	b	c	d	e	f	g	h	i	j	k	l	m

n	o	p	q	r	s	t	u	v	w	x	y	z

Fill in the missing letters of the alphabet.
The first one has been done for you.

a __b__ c   l ___ n

j ___ l   c ___ e

t ___ v   s ___ u

h ___ j   x ___ z

s ___ u   p ___ r

f ___ h   m ___ o

to   going   are   you   no   of   see   they

Notes for teachers
Target: To know the order of the letters of the alphabet

This is an excellent activity for focusing on letter names rather than sounds. Children should be aware that each letter has both a name and a commonly used sound. This activity can be extended by asking children which letters come immediately before and after each of the clusters shown. They can also be asked to suggest a word beginning with each letter of the alphabet.

Name: _____   Date: _____

a b c d e f g h i j k l m n o p q r s t u v w x y z

Join the letters in alphabetical order.

a   q   g   r   n

                          c

        o   p   s   b

f   l

        k   m   h

z   e   u   d

    x   t

j   y   w   v   i

they   going   you   come

    to   are   no   out

Notes for teachers

Target: Alphabetical order in lower case

This is an entertaining game where the child is challenged to join the letters in alphabetical order by drawing lines, starting with the letter a. You may need to suggest to the children that the lines don't have to be straight. If the child finds the task relatively straightforward you can add the element of timing: 'How quickly can you join the letters in alphabetical order?' This can be very successful where children work in pairs, with one child drawing the lines and the other one finding the next letter to join to.

a b c d e f g h i j k l m n o p q r s t u v w x y z

Join the capital letters in alphabetical order.

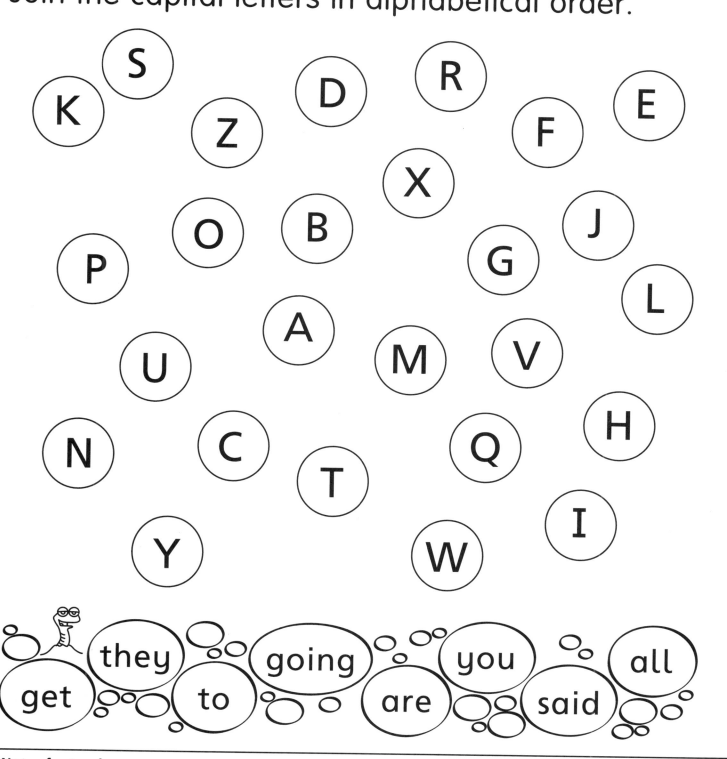

Name: _____   Date: _____

a b c d e f g h i j k l m n o p q r s t u v w x y z

Write the words in alphabetical order.

WORD BANK

king   about   live   dog   from
here   girl   elephant   boy
if   jump   man   cat

1. _____   6. _____   11. _____

2. _____   7. _____   12. _____

3. _____   8. _____   13. _____

4. _____   9. _____

5. _____   10. _____

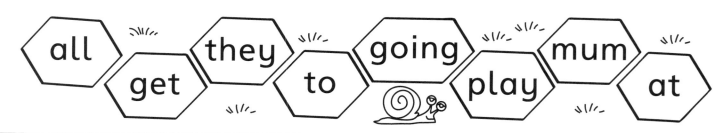

all   they   going   mum
get   to   play   at

Notes for teachers
Target: Writing words in alphabetical order where the initial letters are in lower case
Read each word with the child then encourage him/her to read it alone. Explain that the words can be arranged in alphabetical order so he/she could look first for a word that begins with **a**. Repeat this for **b**, etc. On the worksheet there is a word for each letter from **a** to **m**. The list includes *cat* and *dog* which appear in the set of N L S high frequency words for Reception and *boy, from, girl, here, if, live* and *man*, which appear in the set of high frequency words for Years 1 and 2.

Name: _____ Date: _____

| a b c d e f g h i j k l m n o p q r s t u v w x y z |

Write the words in alphabetical order.

WORD BANK

queen   out   zoo   then   put
ran   x-ray   school   night
us   want   your   very

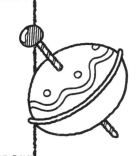

1. _____   6. _____   11. _____

2. _____   7. _____   12. _____

3. _____   8. _____   13. _____

4. _____   9. _____

5. _____   10. _____

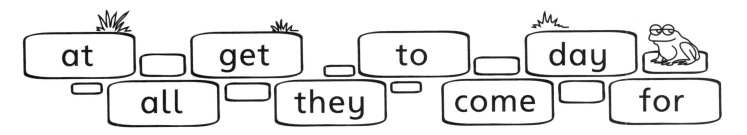

at   all   get   they   to   come   day   for

Notes for teachers
Target: Writing words in alphabetical order where the initial letters are in lower case
This sheet should be used as a follow up to Worksheet 31. Read each word with the child, then encourage him/her to read it
alone. Explain that the words can be arranged in alphabetical order just like on Worksheet 31. Look back at Worksheet 31
and show the child that the words began letters from **a** to **m**. The first word on this worksheet will start with n, so he/she
could look first for a word that begins with **n**. Repeat this for **o** to **z**. All of the words on this sheet, except x-ray, appear in
the list of high frequency words for Years 1 and 2.

Name: _____   Date: _____

a b c d e f g h i j k l m n o p q r s t u v w x y z

Write the words in alphabetical order.

WORD BANK

much   because   good   house

water   people   down   school

called   little   night   very   your

1. _____   6. _____   11. _____

2. _____   7. _____   12. _____

3. _____   8. _____   13. _____

4. _____   9. _____

5. _____   10. _____

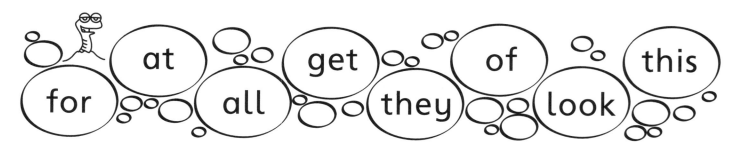

at   get   of   this

for   all   they   look

Notes for teachers

Target: writing words in alphabetical order where the initial letters are in lower case

This sheet can be used as a follow up to Worksheets 31 and 32. Read each word with the child, then encourage him/her to read it alone. Explain that the words can be arranged in alphabetical order just like on the previous worksheets but this time there is not a word for each letter of the alphabet. Encourage the child to look for a word beginning with letter **a**; if there isn't one he/she should move on to letter **b** and so on. This is excellent practice for making use of the alphabet and for practising reading and writing words that appear in the list of high frequency words for Years 1 and 2.

Name: _____   **Date:** _____

Read each word. Copy each word.
Draw the pictures. Colour the pictures.

ring

----

sing

----

wing

----

king

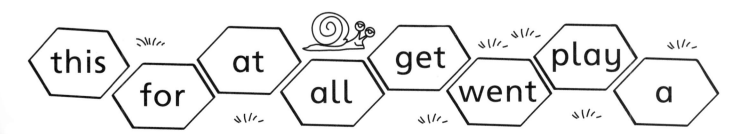

this   for   at   all   get   went   play   a

Notes for teachers
Target: To know the word ending **ng**
After reading the words, children should think of other 'ing' words. You may need to point out that some words have **ing** as part of the word whilst other words have **ing** added to them, e.g. running. Ensure that words are copied with correctly formed letters.

Name: _____

Date: _____

Use some of these words in an interesting sentence.

WORD BANK

bang	song	sang	king
thing	bring	long	gong

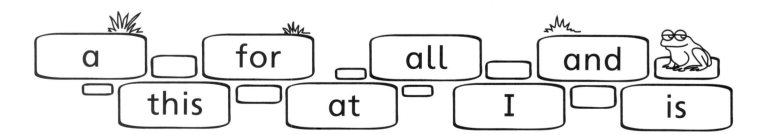

a · for · all · and
this · at · I · is

Notes for teachers
Target: To know the word ending **ng**
Read all the 'ng' words on the page with your group. Ask them to use one of the words in a sentence, e.g. *I can bang a drum.* Children may soon realise that they can use more than one of the words, e.g. *The king sang a long song.* This is to be encouraged and praised. Ask pupils to use the sentence they liked best (of all that you and they made up) and write it carefully on the lines provided. They may need help to correctly spell any words that are not printed on the page. Use of the 'garden path' words may help with the sentence making. There is further practice of this consonant blend on Worksheet 37.

Sort the words from the word bank.

WORD BANK

off   yell   fuss   ball   mess
huff   mill   sniff   miss

.. ss

.. ll

.. ff

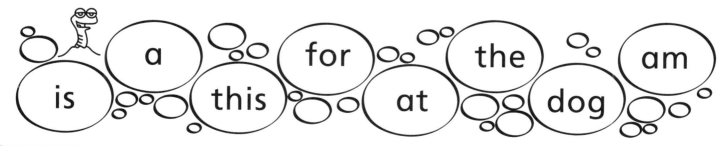

is   a   this   for   at   the   dog   am

Notes for teachers

Target: To know the word endings **ss**, **ff**, **ll**

Read all the words in the word bank with your pupils. Ask them to identify the words that end in **ss**, by referring to the sound and the appearance of the blend. They should write the 'ss' words under the appropriate heading. Now discuss the words that end in **ll** in the same way, then the words that end in **ff**. Notice that there is an extra line in each set for a child to add another word if they can think of one. You may need to give them some ideas to use e.g. *less, kiss, hiss, dress, tall, hill, pull, will, muff, puff.* Ask them to use one of the words from each of the lists in a spoken sentence. If they are confident they could write the sentence down.

Sort the words from the word bank.

WORD BANK

ring	back	old	gold	long
clock	held	tick-tock	sing	

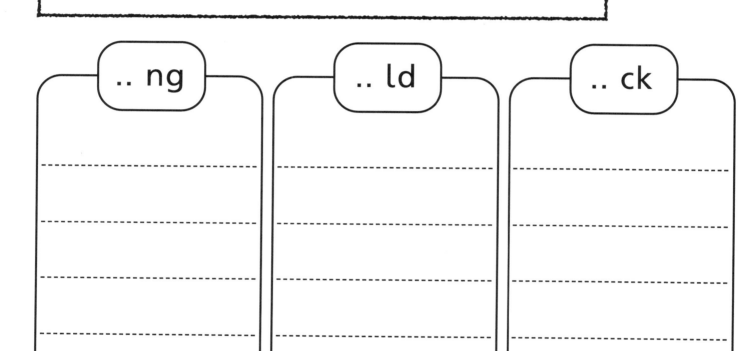

.. ng

.. ld

.. ck

am   is   a   this   for   cat   said   he

Notes for teachers

Target: To know the word endings **ng**, **ck**, **ld**

Read all the words in the word bank with your pupils. Ask them to identify the words that end in **ng**, by referring to the sound and the appearance of the grapheme. They should write the 'ng' words under the appropriate heading. Now discuss the words that end in **ld** in the same way, then the words that end in **ck**. Notice that there is an extra line in each set for a child to add another word if they can think of one. You may need to give them some ideas to use: e.g. *king, bang, wing, song, fold, cold, told, child, pack, sack, peck, lock, duck.* Ask them to use one of the words from each of the lists in a spoken sentence. If they are confident they could write the sentence down .

Name: _____ Date: _____

Sort the words from the word bank.

┌─ **WORD BANK** ──────────────────────────────┐
│   │
│ kind   pink   hulk   think   bend   │
│   │
│ elk   thank   mind   silk   │
│   │
└──┘

.. nd

.. lk

.. nk

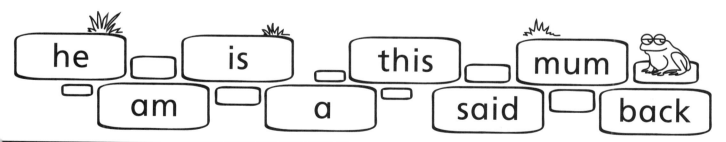

he   is   this   mum

am   a   said   back

Notes for teachers

Target: To know the word endings **nd**, **nk**, **lk**

Read all the words in the word bank with your group. Ask them to identify the words that end in **nd**, by referring to the sound and the appearance of the blend. They should write the 'nd' words under the appropriate heading. Now discuss the words that end in **lk** in the same way, then the words that end in **nk**. Notice that there is an extra line in each set for a child to add another word if they can think of one. You may need to give them some ideas to use e.g. *bind, find, mend, send, band, milk, sulk bulk, wink, bank, tank, ink.* Notice that the letter 'i' has a long sound in words such as kind and a short sound in silk. The children may like to know that an elk is a very large deer found in North America. Ask them to use one of the words from each of the lists together with any of the 'garden path' words in a spoken sentence. If they are confident they could write the sentence down.

43

Name: _____   **Date:** _____

Sort the words from the word bank.

WORD BANK

camp   jazz   tent   plant   fizz

stamp   mint   buzz   limp

.. mp	.. nt	.. zz

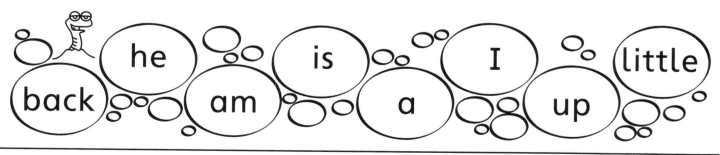

he   is   I   little

back   am   a   up

Notes for teachers
Target: To know the word endings **mp**, **nt**, **zz**

Read all the words in the wordbank with your group. Ask them to identify the words that end in **mp**, by referring to the sound and the appearance of the blend. They should write the **mp** words under the appropriate heading. Now discuss the words that end in **nt** in the same way, then the words that end in **zz**. Notice that there is an extra line in each set for a child to add another word if they can think of one. You may need to give them some ideas to use e.g. *bent, ant, dent, print, fuzz, jump, damp, pump, ramp*. Ask them to use one of the words from each of the lists and any of the 'garden path' words in a spoken sentence. If they are confident they could write the sentence down.

Sort the words from the word bank.

WORD BANK

mask   help   alp   ask   lisp

wisp   risk   yelp   gasp

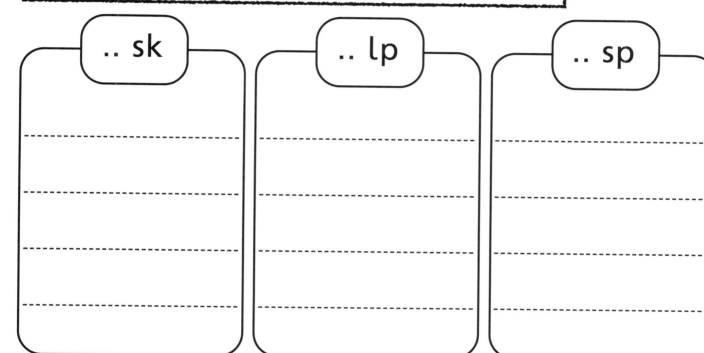

.. sk   .. lp   .. sp

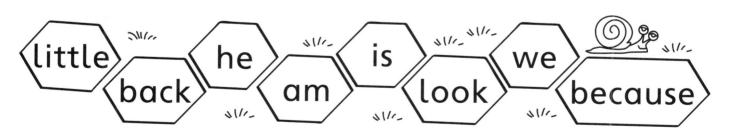

little   back   he   am   is   look   we   because

Notes for teachers

Target: To know the word endings **sk, lp, sp**

Read all the words in the wordbank with your group. Ask them to identify the words that end in **sk,** by referring to the sound and the appearance of the blend. They should write the 'sk' words under the appropriate heading. Now discuss the words that end in **lp** in the same way, then the words that end in **sp**. Notice that there is an extra line in each set for a child to add another word if they can think of one. You may need to give them some ideas to use e.g. *frisk, task, bask, rusk, scalp, crisp.* The children may like to know that 'alp' is a name for a high mountain. Ask them to use one of the words from each of the lists and any of the 'garden path' words in a spoken sentence or written down if they are confident.

Name:

Date:

Sort the words from the word bank.

WORD BANK

raft   park   act   protect   dark

lift   cork   fact   loft

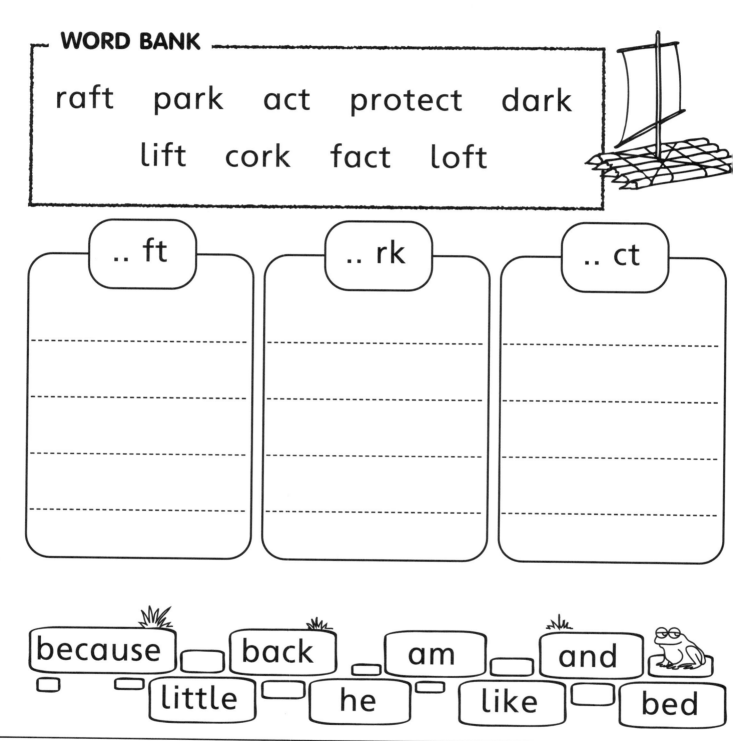

.. ft

.. rk

.. ct

because   back   am   and

little   he   like   bed

Notes for teachers

Target: To know the word endings **ft**, **rk**, **ct**

Read all the words in the word bank with your group. Ask them to identify the words that end in **ft** by referring to the sound and the appearance of the blend. They should write the 'ft' words under the appropriate heading. Now discuss the words that end in **rk** in the same way, then the words that end in **ct**. There is an extra line in each set for a child to add another word if they can think of one. You may need to give them some ideas to use e.g. *lark, jerk, bark, mark, perk, tact, pact, duct, impact, inspect, left, tuft, daft, gift.* You could discuss the fact that some of the words have two syllables: *protect, impact, inspect.* You could use the opportunity to discuss syllables, e.g. the number of syllables in each child's name. Encourage the children to 'hear' the syllables by clapping them. Ask them to use one of the words from each of the lists and any of the 'garden path' words in a spoken sentence or, if they are confident, they could write the sentence down.

Andrew Brodie: Supporting Literacy © A & C Black Publishers Ltd. 2006

Sort the words from the word bank.

WORD BANK

adult	next	self	wolf
melt	quilt	text	elf

.. lt

.. xt

.. lf

because   back   on   boy

bed   little   he   at

Notes for teachers

Target: To know the word endings **lt, xt, lf**

Read all the words in the word bank with your group. Ask them to identify the words that end in **lt**, by referring to the sound and the appearance of the blend. They should write the 'lt' words under the appropriate heading. It would be useful to point out the spelling of 'quilt' as it shows how the letter **q** operates with the letter **u**.

Discuss the words that end in **xt** in the same way, then the words that end in **lf**. Please note that there are only two lines under **xt** as there are so few words that end with this blend. There is an extra line in each set for a child to add another word if they can think of one. You may need to give them some ideas to use e.g. *pelt, belt, felt, bolt, colt, gulf, golf.* Children may be able to hear the 'xt' sound in some other words where the **xt** blend is not at the end e.g. *mixture.* They should be praised for any suggestion like this. Ask them to use one of the words from each of the lists and any of the 'garden path' words in a spoken sentence or, if they are confident, they could write the sentence down.

Name: _____   **Date:** _____

Sort the words from the word bank.

WORD BANK

glad   plug   blast   blot   play

glass   plum   blush   glide

bl ..	gl ..	pl ..

boy   bed   because   little   back   for   he   house

Notes for teachers

Target: To know the initial blends **bl**, **gl**, **pl**

Read all the words in the word bank with your group. Ask them to identify the words that start with **bl** by referring to the sound and the appearance of the blend. They should write the **bl** words under the appropriate heading. The words **blast** and **blush** also provide practice of the endings **st** and **sh**. Discuss the words that begin with **gl** in the same way, then the words that begin with **pl**. Notice that there is an extra line in each set for a child to add another word if they can think of one. You may need to give them some ideas to use e.g. *black, blob, globe, glue, please, plan, playing, plop, plot*. Ask them to use one of the words from each of the lists and any of the 'garden path' words in a spoken sentence or, if they are confident, they could write the sentence down.

Name: _____   **Date:** _____

Sort the words from the word bank.

WORD BANK

brass   dry   crab   dress   brown

crisp   cry   brain   drain

br ..	cr ..	dr ..
-----	-----	-----
-----	-----	-----
-----	-----	-----
-----	-----	-----

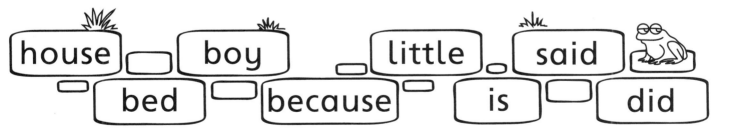

house   bed   boy   because   little   is   said   did

Notes for teachers

Target: To know the initial blends **br**, **cr**, **dr**

Read all the words in the word bank with your group. Ask them to identify the words that start with **br** by referring to the sound and the appearance of the blend. They should write the **br** words under the appropriate heading. The word 'brass' provides practice with the ending **ss**; 'brown' is a key colour word – the children may need some support with reading the vowel consonant digraph **ow**; the word 'brain' features the common vowel digraph **ai**. You could also point this out in the word 'drain'. Discuss the words that begin with **cr** and **dr** in the same way. There is an extra line in each set for a child to add another word if they can think of one. You may need to give them some ideas to use e.g. *brick, bring, bread, bran, crust, cross, crush, drip, drop, drum.* Ask them to use one of the words from each of the lists and any of the 'garden path' words in a spoken sentence or, if they are confident, they could write the sentence down.

Sort the words from the word bank.

WORD BANK

scab   swim   skip   scoop   skin

swing   sweet   scoot   sky

sw ..	sc ..	sk ..

house   bed   go   make

did   boy   because   you

Notes for teachers

Target: To know the initial blends **sw**, **sc**, **sk**

Read all the words in the word bank with your group. Ask them to identify the words that start with **sw**, by referring to the sound and the appearance of the blend. They should write the **sw** words under the appropriate heading. Discuss the words that begin with **sc** and **sk** in the same way. There is an extra line in each set for a child to add another word if they can think of one. You may need to give them some ideas to use e.g. *swan, swarm, sweep, scout, scarf, scooter, skid, skill, skim.* Encourage the children to see links between the words e.g. sweep and sweet, scoot and scoop, scoot and scooter. Ask them to use one of the words from each of the lists and any of the 'garden path' words in a spoken sentence or, If they are confident, they could write it down.

Sort the words from the word bank.

WORD BANK

| grab | print | slab | slip | grip |

| grass | slid | pram | prod |

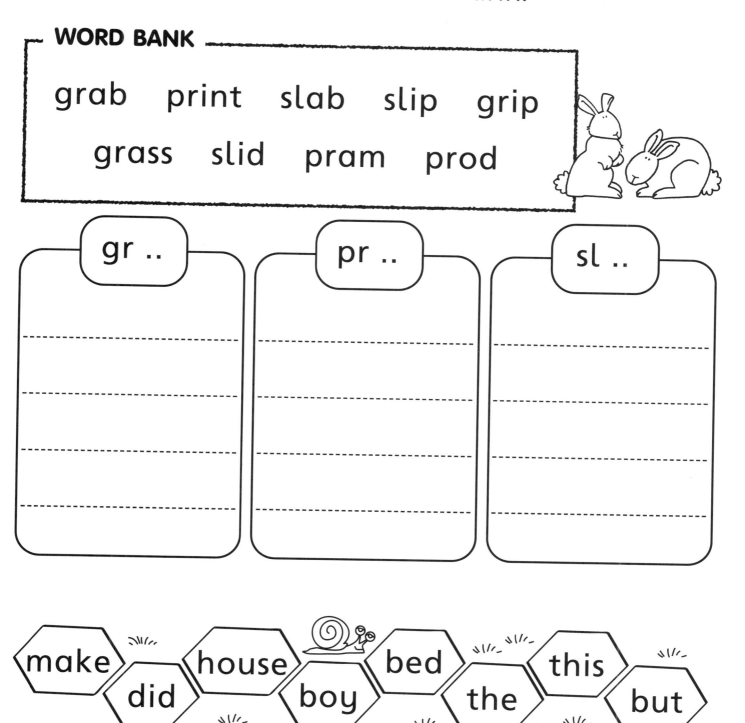

gr ..

pr ..

sl ..

make   did   house   boy   bed   the   this   but

Notes for teachers

Target: To know the initial blends **gr**, **pr**, **sl**

Read all the words in the word bank with your group. Ask them to identify the words that start with **gr** by referring to the sound nand the appearance of the blend. They should write the **gr** words under the appropriate heading. Discuss the words that begin with **pr** and **sl** in the same way. There is an extra line in each set to enable you to ask the child to think of another word for the list. You may need to give them some ideas to use e.g. *grill, grin, grain, pray, present, press, pretend, slam, slap, slide, sling.* 'Present' and 'pretend' are both two-syllable words. This would provide an opportunity to discuss syllables with the children. Ask them to use one of the words from each of the lists and any of the 'garden path' words in a spoken sentence or, if they are confident, they could write the sentence down.

Name: **Date:**

Sort the words from the word bank.

WORD BANK

small   sniff   space   snip   spell

spill   smell   smoke   snow

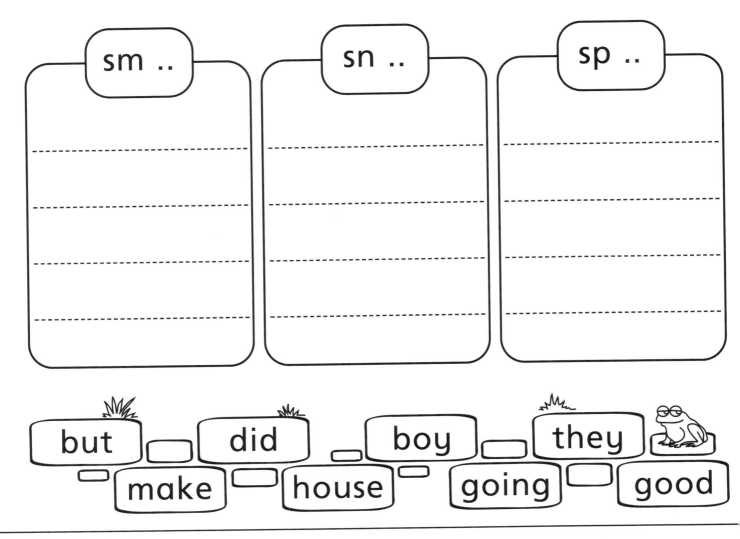

sm ..

sn ..

sp ..

but   did   boy   they

make   house   going   good

Notes for teachers

Target: To know the initial blends **sm, sn, sp**

Read all the words in the word bank with your group. Ask them to identify the words that start with **sm** by referring to the sound and the appearance of the blend. They should write the **sm** words under the appropriate heading. Discuss the words that begin with **sn** and **sp** in the same way. There is an extra line in each set for a child to add another word if they can think of one. You may need to give them some ideas to use e.g. *smart, smash, snap, snug, spade, span, spin, speck, speak, speed, spot, spy.* Encourage the children to see links between the words e.g. spell and spill, spell and smell, smell and small, spin and spill. Ask them to use one of the words from each of the lists and any of the 'garden path' words in a spoken sentence or, if they are confident, they could write the sentence down.

Andrew Brodie: Supporting Literacy © A & C Black Publishers Ltd. 2006

Name: _____ **Date:** _____

┌─ **WORD BANK** ──────────────────────────────┐
│   │
│   flower   stem   leaf   roots   soil   pot │
│   │
└──┘

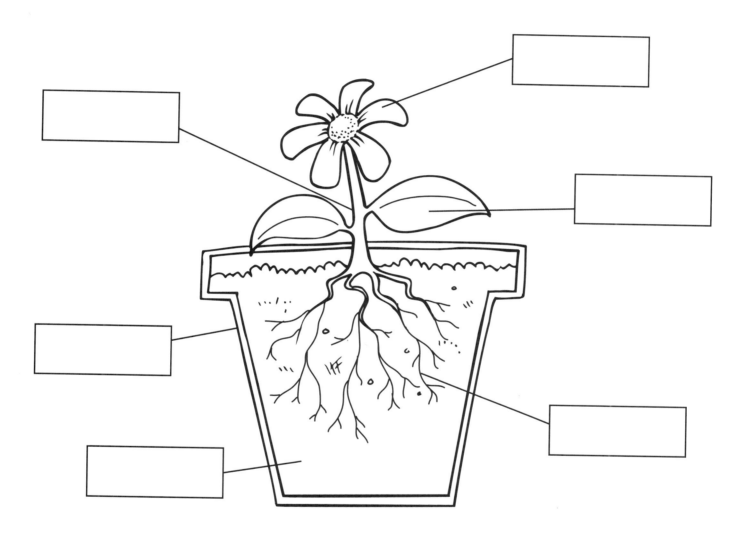

Plants need water to help them grow.
Plants need light to help them grow.

Notes for teachers
Target: To read and write words needed in science work on growing plants
Look carefully at the picture with the child ensuring that he/she understands completely that the picture shows a plant growing in soil in a pot, that the plant has roots in the soil and that it has a stem, leaves and a flower. Read the two sentences to the child then ask him/her to read them to you. Ask the child to label the picture using words from the word bank. You may like to take the opportunity to practise words with similar blends to those in the word bank:
fl – flower, fly, flag, flip, flop, fling, etc, **st** – stop, step, sting, stir, etc, **ea** – tea, sea, heat, team, read, eat, etc, (but not head, bread, etc) **oo** – boot, food, tooth, pool, hoot, etc, (but not look, foot, etc).

Andrew Brodie: Supporting Literacy © A & C Black Publishers Ltd. 2006

Name: _____   **Date:** _____

Use the words to label the picture.

WORD BANK

cliff   sea   beach   pier   sandcastle

boy   girl   sky   sun   cloud

Notes for teachers

This sheet can be used with Year 2 pupils studying 'the seaside' in geography and history. Look carefully at the picture with the child. Encourage him/her to discuss what can be seen in the picture, then discuss the words in the word bank before he/she attempts to label the picture. After the picture has been labelled, you could ask the child to identify common patterns in the words e.g. Which of the words begin with **s**? Which of the words begin with **cl**? Can you think of other words that begin with **cl**?

cl: *clap, clip, clock, club, cling, clever, etc*   **sk**: *skip, skin, skid, etc*

In your next lesson the child could use this Worksheet with Worksheet 50.

Andrew Brodie: Supporting Literacy © A & C Black Publishers Ltd. 2006

Look at the picture on worksheet 49.
Answer the questions.

1. What people can you see on the beach?

----

2. What else is on the beach?

----

3. What is in the sky?

----

4. What building can you see?

Notes for teachers
Target: To write complete sentences
These questions are designed for use with the picture and words on Resource Sheet D and can be related to Year 2 work on
'the seaside'. Read each question to the child and ask him or her to repeat the question. Discuss the question and the picture
then encourage the child to write each answer in a full sentence, with a capital letter at the start and a full stop at the end.
For example, for question 1 the child could write: _I can see a girl and a boy on the beach._ or _There is a boy and a girl on the_
beach. Alternatively a simple four-page book could be made with a sentence on each page and an illustration by the child to
go with it.

NLS High frequency words recommended for Reception

a	all	am
and	are	at
away	big	can
cat	come	dad
day	dog	for
get	go	going
he	I	in
is	it	like

Notes for teachers
These can be photocopied and laminated before being cut out and used as flashcards, for making sentences and for playing games such as 'snap'.

NLS High frequency words recommended for Reception

look	me	mum
my	no	of
on	play	said
see	she	the
they	this	to
up	was	we
went	yes	you

Notes for teachers
These can be photocopied and laminated before being cut out and used as flashcards, for making sentences and for playing games such as 'snap'.

about	after	again
an	another	as
back	ball	be
because	bed	been
boy	brother	but
by	call	called
came	can't	could
did	do	don't

Notes for teachers

These can be photocopied and laminated before being cut out and used as flashcards, for making sentences and for playing games such as 'snap'.

NLS High frequency words recommended for Y1 and Y2

dig	door	down
first	from	girl
good	got	had
half	has	have
help	her	here
him	his	home
house	how	if
jump	just	last

Notes for teachers
These can be photocopied and laminated before being cut out and used as flashcards, for making sentences and for playing games such as 'snap'.

NLS High frequency words recommended for Y1 and Y2

laugh	little	live
lived	love	made
make	man	many
may	more	much
must	name	new
next	night	not
now	off	old
once	one	or

Notes for teachers
These can be photocopied and laminated before being cut out and used as flashcards, for making sentences and for playing games such as 'snap'.

NLS High frequency words recommended for Y1 and Y2

our	out	over
people	push	pull
put	ran	saw
school	seen	should
sister	so	some
take	than	that
their	them	then
there	these	three

Notes for teachers
These can be photocopied and laminated before being cut out and used as flashcards, for making sentences and for playing games such as 'snap'.

NLS High frequency words recommended for Y1 and Y2

time	too	took
tree	two	us
very	want	water
way	were	what
when	where	who
will	with	would
your		

Notes for teachers

In addition to the list of high frequency words, the NLS also suggests that pupils should learn to read their own name and address and the name and address of the school. You may like to use the five 'spare' tiles on this sheet to write the main words of the school address, in particular the street name and the town name.

NLS High frequency words recommended for Y1 and Y2

four	five	six
seven	eight	nine
ten	eleven	twelve
thirteen	fourteen	fifteen
sixteen	seventeen	eighteen
nineteen	twenty	Monday
Tuesday	Wednesday	Thursday
Friday	Saturday	Sunday

Notes for teachers

In addition to the list of high frequency words recommended for Year 1 and Year 2, the NLS also suggests that pupils should learn to read numbers to twenty, days of the week, months of the year and colours. Numbers one, two and three are already included in the list of high frequency words.

January	February	March
April	May	June
July	August	September
October	November	December
week	year	black
white	red	blue
green	yellow	orange
pink	brown	purple

Notes for teachers

In addition to the list of high frequency words recommended for Year 1 and Year 2, the NLS also suggests that pupils should learn to read numbers to twenty, days of the week, months of the year and colours. We have also included the words 'week' and 'year'.